nickelodeon™
TEENAGE MUTANT NINJA TURTLES™

1000
Stickers

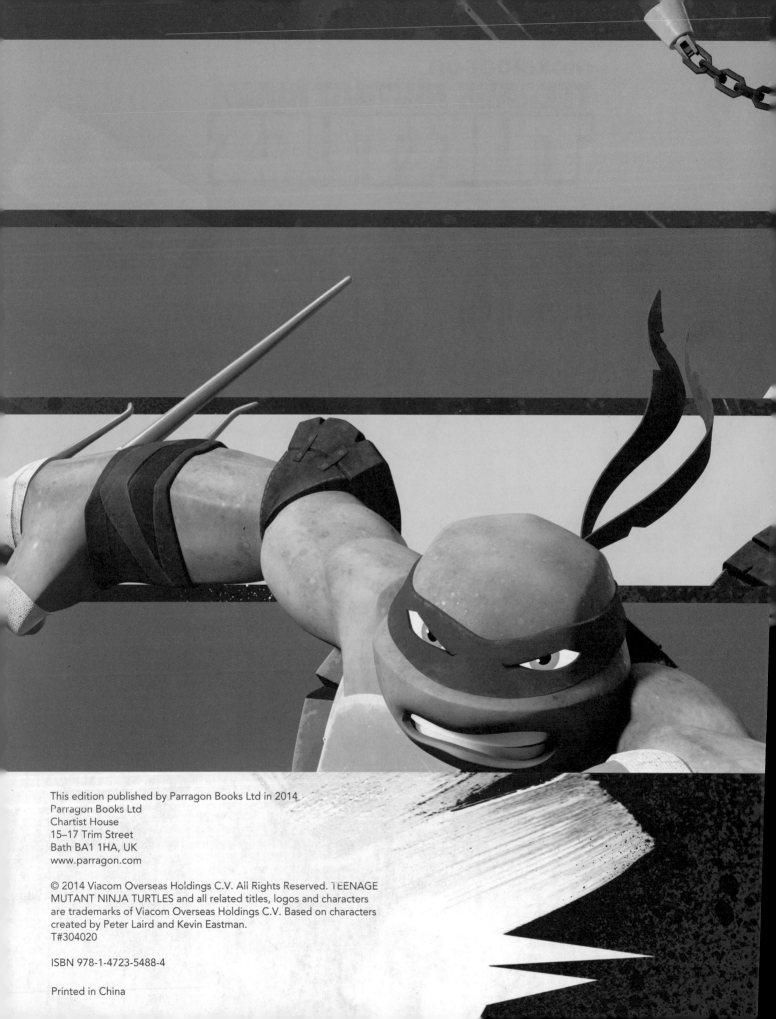

This edition published by Parragon Books Ltd in 2014
Parragon Books Ltd
Chartist House
15–17 Trim Street
Bath BA1 1HA, UK
www.parragon.com

ISBN 978-1-4723-5488-4

Printed in China

PaRragon

Bath · New York · Cologne · Melbourne · Delhi
Hong Kong · Shenzhen · Singapore · Amsterdam

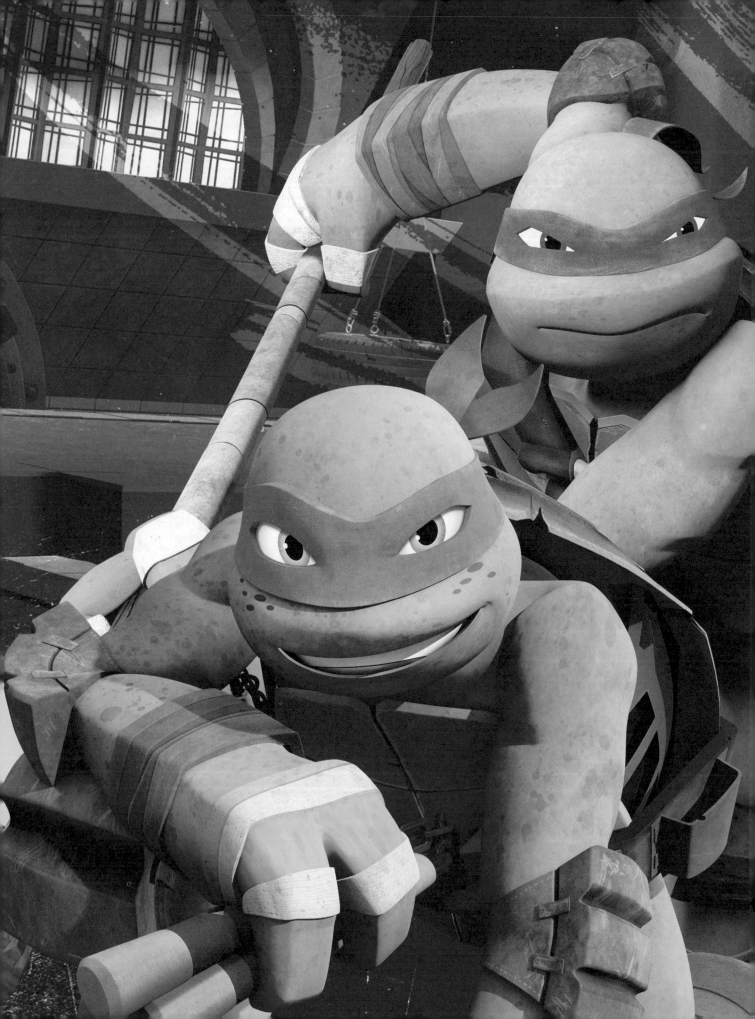

COLOURING PAGES

THE TURTLES LIVE IN THE DARK SEWERS BELOW NEW YORK CITY.
BRING SOME COLOUR INTO THEIR WORLD!

LEAN, MEAN AND GREEN

"We're heroes, that's what heroes do."

LEONARDO

"Failure is not an option!"

MICHELANGELO

"Dr Prankenstein ... with nunchucks!"

DONATELLO

"Who are you calling a shellbrain?"

SURFACE TIME!

Nothing stops the Turtles when they fight as a team.

SHREDDER

"I want them all wiped out."

FOOT CLAN

"From the shadows to the streets."

SPLINTER

"Showing mercy is a sign of strength."

APRIL

"Don't stand between me and my dad."

THE KRAANG

"We will colonize the Earth!"

KRAANG-DROID

A walking weapon.

FISHFACE

His kick is as bad as his bite.

DOGPOUND

A hellhound with dog breath.

THE PATROL BUGGY

Another epic Donnie invention.

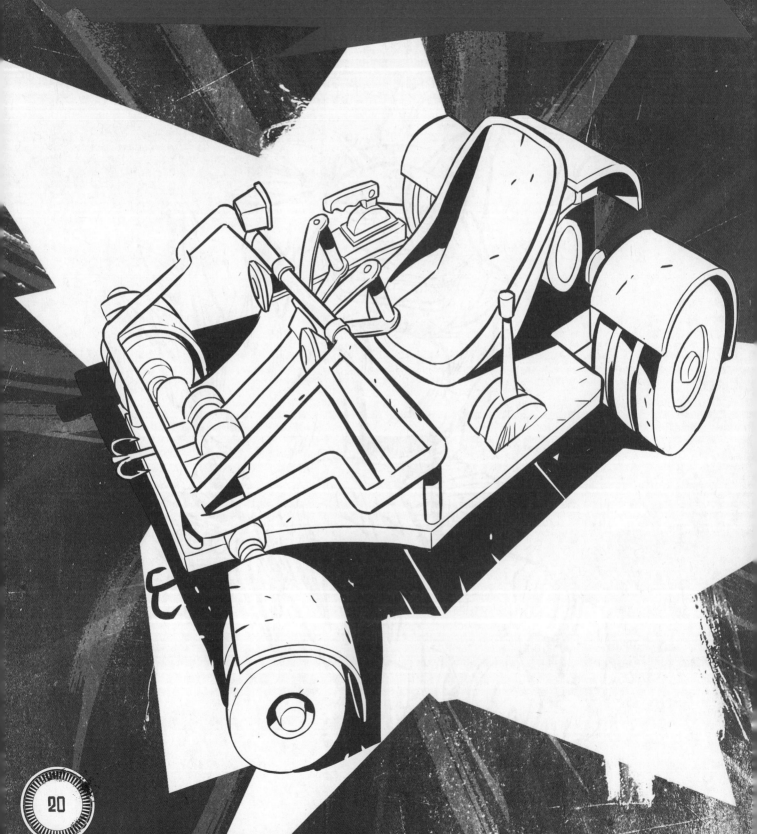

THE SHELLRAISER

Armed and dangerous.

ACTIVITY PAGES

DUDES, IT'S TIME TO GET BUSY! HELP THE TURTLES ANSWER MIND-BENDING QUESTIONS AND SOLVE AWESOME PUZZLES – NINJA-STYLE.

IT'S TEST TIME, SHELL-BRAINS!

How well do you know the Turtles? Take the test to see if you're a loyal follower or a wannabe fan.

1 Who is the leader?

A] MICHELANGELO
B] LEONARDO
C] RAPHAEL

2 What is the Turtles' favourite food?

A] ALGAE
B] PIZZA
C] LETTUCE

3 Who has a pet turtle called Spike?

A] MICHELANGELO
B] DONATELLO
C] RAPHAEL

4 Which Turtle fights with the Katanas (double swords)?

A] LEONARDO
B] RAPHAEL
C] MICHELANGELO

5 The Turtles do their ninja training in a ...

A] BOHO
B] YOYO
C] DOJO

N.Y.C.

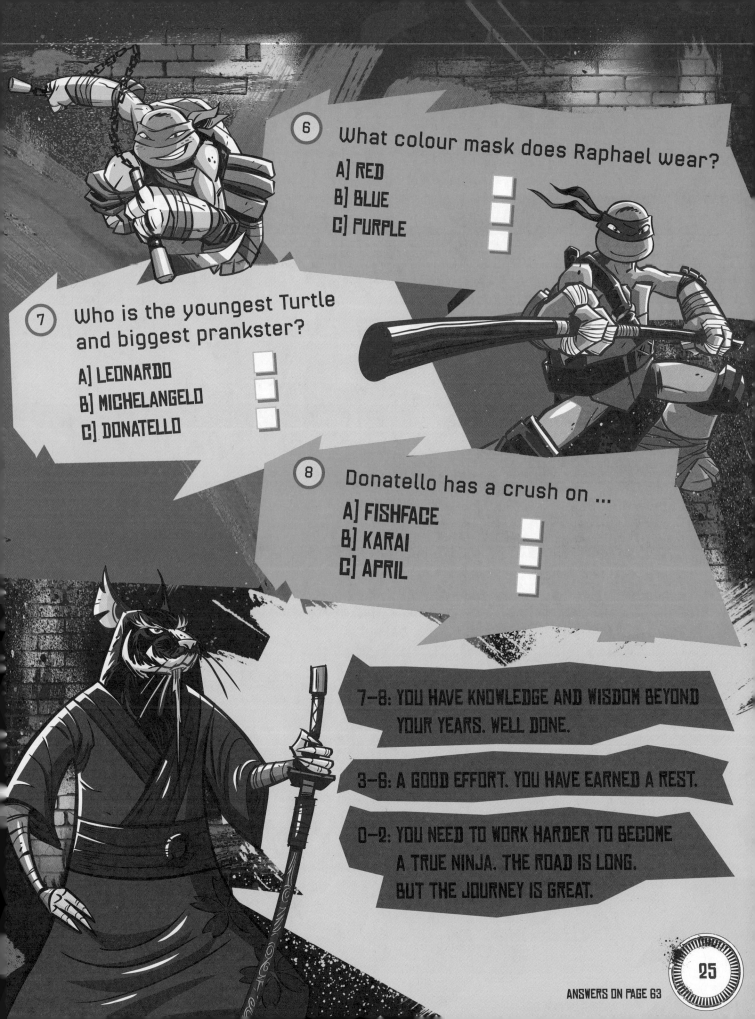

6 What colour mask does Raphael wear?
A] RED
B] BLUE
C] PURPLE

7 Who is the youngest Turtle and biggest prankster?
A] LEONARDO
B] MICHELANGELO
C] DONATELLO

8 Donatello has a crush on ...
A] FISHFACE
B] KARAI
C] APRIL

7–8: YOU HAVE KNOWLEDGE AND WISDOM BEYOND YOUR YEARS. WELL DONE.

3–6: A GOOD EFFORT. YOU HAVE EARNED A REST.

0–2: YOU NEED TO WORK HARDER TO BECOME A TRUE NINJA. THE ROAD IS LONG. BUT THE JOURNEY IS GREAT.

SENSEI STEALTH

Splinter is a master of stealth and disguise.
Can you find him in this picture?

ANSWER ON PAGE 63

SENSEI WISDOM

Which of these things would Splinter NOT say?

1 IT'S NOT ABOUT WINNING AND LOSING. IT'S ABOUT SELF-IMPROVEMENT.

YES NO

2 IT IS YOU WHO MUST PREVAIL IN BATTLE, NOT YOUR WEAPON.

YES NO

3 WE WILL TAKE OVER THIS PLANET THAT IS CALLED 'EARTH'.

YES NO

4 MAKE THEM BEG FOR MERCY!

YES NO

5 A NINJA'S MOST POWERFUL WEAPON IS THE SHADOWS.

YES NO

ANSWERS ON PAGE 63

DR PRANKENSTEIN

Mikey has pranked his brothers once too often and now it's payback time! They all fling a water balloon at him but which Turtle scores a direct hit?

ANSWER ON PAGE 63

MAKE A MUTANT

What's your favourite animal? How would it look if it were hit with ooze and mutated? Draw it here!

- Would your mutant have robotic parts?
- Or gross oozy bits?
- Is it heavily armed or a stealthy ninja?
- Is it good or evil?

SHRED THE SHREDDER

It's a full-on fight between the Turtles and Shredder!
Five things have changed in the bottom picture.
Colour one ninja star each time you find a difference.

30

SEWER SCRAMBLE

After a day of bot-bashing, the Turtles are looking forward to shellaxing in the lair. But which manhole should they take?

ANSWER ON PAGE 63

NINJA DISGUISE

Can you tell who is who? Colour in the Turtles' masks before checking if you're right.

ANSWERS ON PAGE 63

THE ART OF OBSERVATION

Some people cannot see what is right in front of them.
Test your ninja skills by finding these words in the grid.
Look forwards, backwards, up, down and diagonally.

dojo

hajime

hero

justice

ninja

power

sensei

shadow

stealth

sword

E M E N S T O Q Q H
O M C I Y H R J T H
R X I N X P A L O I
E T T J V Z A D V D
H J S A A E X D O Q
K K U Y T H O X P W
I H J S K S H O C R
S E N S E I W N E U
D R O W S E R K Z I
I T I F R C Q J D N

PREPARE FOR BATTLE

Ninjas need to be battle-ready at all times, but the Turtles are only fully prepared in two of these pictures. Colour in the correct two ninja stars.

ANSWERS ON PAGE 63

HOW TO DRAW A TURTLE

Copy this picture of Michelangelo.
Use the grid to help you!

NOW ADD SOME COLOUR TO
YOUR NUNCHUCK HERO!

IF YOU WERE A TURTLE ...

... who would you be? Answer these questions to find out....

How strong are you?

A] I'M AS TOUGH AS A TURTLE SHELL!
B] I'M STRONG IN MIND AND SPIRIT
C] BRAINS BEAT MUSCLES ANY DAY
D] I'M WORKING ON IT!

You're riding in the Shellraiser - would you ...

A] MAN THE WEAPONS
B] DRIVE
C] BE THE CHIEF ENGINEER
D] TELL THE DRIVER WHERE TO GO

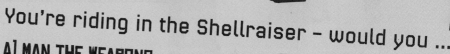

If you're angry, what do you do?

A] BLOW A FUSE
B] TALK ABOUT IT
C] GO TO YOUR ROOM
D] EAT PIZZA

Which word best describes you?

A] LOUD
B] RESPONSIBLE
C] CLEVER
D] FRIENDLY

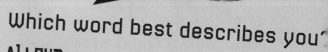

To relax you like to...

A] SPEND TIME WITH YOUR PETS
B] PLAY VIDEO GAMES
C] BUILD THINGS
D] PLAY PRANKS ON YOUR
    BROTHERS AND SISTERS

You're surrounded by enemies, what do you do?

A] GET BUSY BASHING THOSE BADDIES
B] THINK OF A CLEVER PLAN TO BEAT THEM ... THEN BEAT THEM!
C] BACK UP YOUR BROTHERS
D] GET READY FOR SOME FUN!

HOW DID YOU DO?

MOSTLY As

YOU ARE LIKE RAPHAEL. YOU'RE TOUGH, STRONG AND HOT-HEADED. YOUR FRIENDS FEEL SAFE AROUND YOU, BUT YOU ACT BEFORE YOU THINK. THIS CAN SOMETIMES GET YOU INTO BIG TROUBLE!

MOSTLY Bs

YOU ARE LIKE LEONARDO. YOU ARE A LEADER – SMART, THOUGHTFUL AND RESPONSIBLE. YOU'RE ALWAYS THERE FOR YOUR FRIENDS, BUT YOU SHOULD SOMETIMES LISTEN TO THEM MORE.

MOSTLY Cs

YOU ARE LIKE DONATELLO. YOU ARE SUPER CLEVER AND YOUR FRIENDS LOOK UP TO YOU BECAUSE YOU ALWAYS HAVE THE ANSWERS. BUT YOU'RE NOT ALWAYS CONFIDENT AROUND OTHERS AND LIKE TIME ON YOUR OWN.

MOSTLY Ds

YOU ARE LIKE MICHELANGELO. YOU ARE FRIENDLY, ENERGETIC AND FUN-LOVING. YOU'RE THE JOKER AMONG YOUR FRIENDS AND YOU MAKE THEM LAUGH, BUT YOU DON'T ALWAYS THINK THINGS THROUGH.

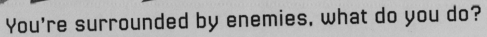

FISHFACE MALFUNCTION

Five parts of Fishface have changed in the bottom picture.
Can you find and circle them all?

ANSWERS ON PAGE 63

SAY WHAT?!

Finish these Turtle sayings by choosing the right word.

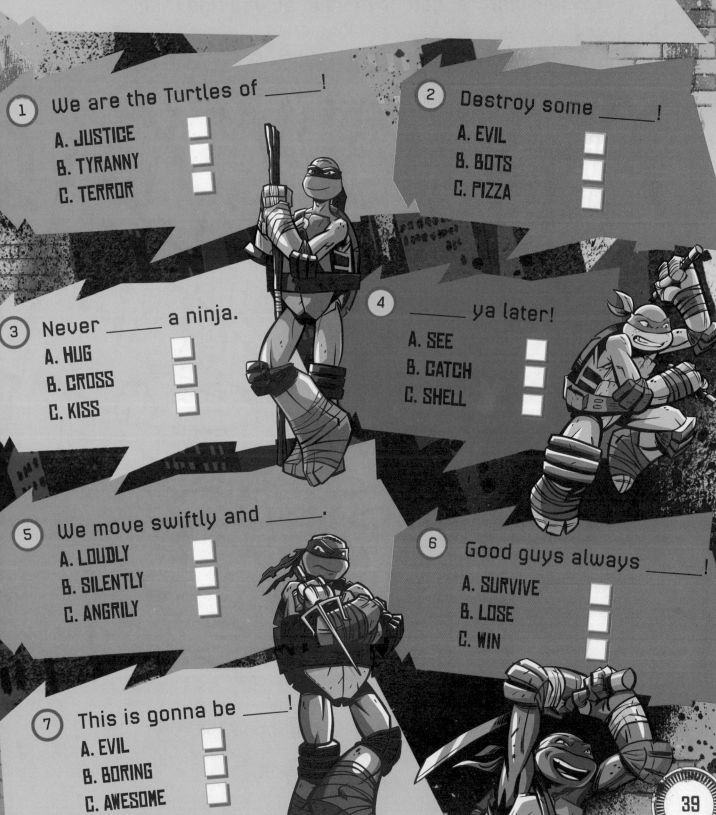

1. We are the Turtles of _____!
   - A. JUSTICE
   - B. TYRANNY
   - C. TERROR

2. Destroy some _____!
   - A. EVIL
   - B. BOTS
   - C. PIZZA

3. Never _____ a ninja.
   - A. HUG
   - B. CROSS
   - C. KISS

4. _____ ya later!
   - A. SEE
   - B. CATCH
   - C. SHELL

5. We move swiftly and _____.
   - A. LOUDLY
   - B. SILENTLY
   - C. ANGRILY

6. Good guys always _____!
   - A. SURVIVE
   - B. LOSE
   - C. WIN

7. This is gonna be _____!
   - A. EVIL
   - B. BORING
   - C. AWESOME

ANSWERS ON PAGE 64

FIND THE MUTAGEN

There are 10 hidden canisters of mutagen in this picture. Colour them in as you find them.

Now colour in the whole scene.

SAME OLD KRAANG

The Kraang all look the same to the Turtles! Which one of the pictures below exactly matches this picture?

ANSWER ON PAGE 64

STICKER ACTIVITY PAGES

IT'S TIME TO STICK IT TO 'EM! FIND THE STICKERS AT THE FRONT OF THE BOOK AND COMPLETE THESE AWESOME ACTIVITIES.

SQUARED UP

This is a game to play with a friend. Choose Leo or Raph from the sticker pages at the front of the book.
Take it in turns to draw one line – horizontal or vertical – that joins two dots. If the line you draw completes a square, you can place one of your stickers in that square.
Whoever has the most stickers on the page at the end is the winner.
It's go time!

EXTREME CLOSE-UP

It's New York at night – it can be hard to tell who's a friend and who's an enemy! Use your stickers and place the full image of each character next to the close-up image.

A

B

C

D

?

?

?

?

45

THE BAD GUYS

Ninjas need to know their enemy.
Use your stickers to match the enemies to
their descriptions.

1

Deadly, cold and ruthless, he is the leader
of the Foot Clan. Human, but without a shred
of humanity.

2

Vicious brain-like aliens set on taking over
the world.

3

A cyber-body created by the Kraang so they
can mix with humans. The Kraang hide inside
their chests.

4

Also known as Chris Bradford.
A famous martial artist turned huge mutant
dog. He is Shredder's main henchman.

ANSWERS ON PAGE 64

CHOOSE YOUR WEAPON

Each Turtle is describing his weapon of choice.
Add the sticker to the right description.

(A)

I USE THE KATANAS, OR DOUBLE SWORDS.
WITH THEM, I CAN DEFEND AND ATTACK AT THE SAME TIME.

?

(B)

I FIGHT WITH THE BO STAFF.
WITH MY LONG TURTLE LIMBS I CAN GET
ENOUGH POWER TO BASH THOSE BOTS TO BITS!

?

(C)

THE NUNCHUCKS ARE MY WEAPON OF CHOICE.
I'M FAST AND AGILE, SO I CAN SPIN THEM AND
SWING THEM FOR MAXIMUM DROID DAMAGE.

?

(D)

I FIGHT WITH THE SAI. THEY ARE THREE-PRONGED DAGGERS.
A PERFECT WEAPON FOR MY FAST TURTLE FISTS.

?

WHAT'S HAPPENING, DUDE?

There's trouble afoot but what exactly is going down?
Find the stickers that match the shadows to find out!

NINJA MOVES

It's training time and Master Splinter has asked each Turtle to practise his moves. Help the Turtles with their ninja training by completing the sequences with your stickers.

ANSWERS ON PAGE 64

OOZE CONTROL

Turtle adventures don't get more epic than this!
Use your stickers to complete the story.

DONATELLO IS IN THE LAB, WORKING ON HIS PATROL BUGGY. *SPLASH!* MIKEY HITS HIM WITH A WATER BALLOON. "DR PRANKENSTEIN STRIKES AGAIN!"

APRIL ARRIVES WITH NEWS THAT SHREDDER IS PLANNING TO DESTROY THE LAIR. THEY HEAD TO THE SURFACE TO FIND OUT WHAT SHREDDER IS UP TO BUT THE FOOT CLAN KIDNAPS APRIL!

THE TURTLES DISCOVER A TANKER FULL OF A STRANGE CHEMICAL THAT EXPLODES WHEN IT TOUCHES WATER. SHREDDER PLANS TO POUR IT INTO THE CITY'S WATER SUPPLY! THE BATTLE IS ON!

THE TANKER GETS AWAY BUT THE TURTLES ARE RIGHT BEHIND IN THE PATROL BUGGY.

DONATELLO PULLS A LEVER AND THE PATROL BUGGY SPLITS IN HALF! DONNIE AND RAPHAEL ZOOM OFF TO SAVE APRIL WHILE LEO AND MIKEY TRY TO STOP THE TANKER.

WHEN THEY FIND THE TANKER, TWO FOOT SOLDIERS ARE ABOUT TO PUMP THE CHEMICAL INTO THE SEWERS AND BLOW UP THE ENTIRE CITY!

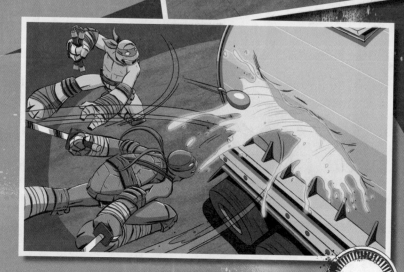

LEO SLASHES THE TANKER AND THE CHEMICAL STARTS GUSHING OUT – MIKEY THROWS A WATER BALLOON. ON CONTACT WITH THE WATER ... *KABOOM!* ... THE TANKER EXPLODES AND THE TURTLES DEFEAT THE FOOT CLAN ONCE MORE!

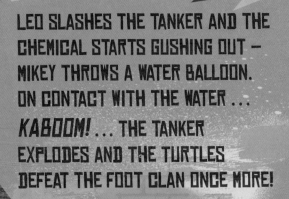

FUNNY FACE

Michelangelo is a funny party dude. Can you complete these pictures of him using your stickers?

DIFFERENT DROIDS

All Kraang-droids are usually identical but these two have five differences. Help Donatello to identify the differences. Add a high-three sticker for each difference you find.

ANSWERS ON PAGE 64

MISSING IN ACTION

It looks like one of the awesome foursome is missing after a battle with Shredder. Which Turtle doesn't appear in the puzzle pieces below? Use your mask stickers to mark the missing hero.

ANSWER ON PAGE 64

ENEMIES IN YOUR SIGHTS

Look at these targets for 30 seconds, then close your eyes and attempt to stick a ninja star on the bad guys. But be careful not to hit April!

KRAANG KOUNTER

The Turtles have found the Kraang's secret hideout!
Count all the Kraang you can see.
Put a high-three sticker next to the correct number.

10

13

16

ANSWER ON PAGE 64

A-MAZE-ING SKILLS

April has been kidnapped by the Foot Clan and Donnie is on his way to rescue her. Use your stickers to complete Donnie's path between the pipes and rescue April.

START →

?

?

?

?

→ FINISH

ANSWERS ON PAGE 64

NINJA TRAINING

A great ninja must have excellent powers of observation. Which of these shadows perfectly matches the image of Master Splinter? Put your Splinter sticker in the right place.

ANSWER ON PAGE 64

THE SHELLRAISER

The Shellraiser has been bashed up in battle!
Help Donatello fix it and make it
combat ready again!

ANGER MANAGEMENT

Raph got angry and smashed this picture.
Now he's calmed down, he wants to put it back together.
Can you help him put the missing pieces in place?

SPOT THE KRAANG-DROID

In a fight against the Kraang, a keen eye is needed. Can you spot the two images of the Kraang-droids that are the same? Mark the real Kraang with some mutagen.

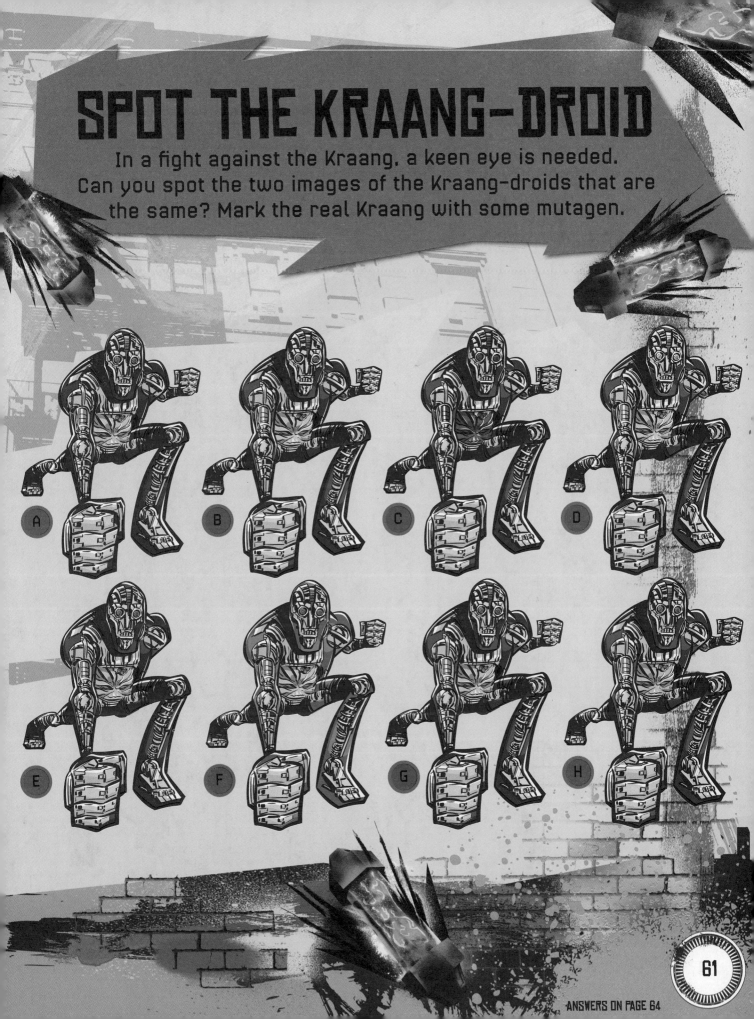

A B C D

E F G H

ANSWERS ON PAGE 64

SHADOW HUNTER

The bad guys are always lurking in the shadows!
Use your ninja skills to shed some light on them by matching
the correct bad guy sticker to the shadow.

ANSWERS

PAGES 24-25

1. B 2. B 3. C 4. A
5. C 6. A 7. B 8. C

PAGE 26

PAGE 27

1. Y 2. Y 3. N 4. N 5. Y

PAGE 28

Leonardo

PAGE 30

PAGE 31

2

PAGE 32

1. Donatello 2. Michelangelo
3. Raphael 4. Leonardo

PAGE 33

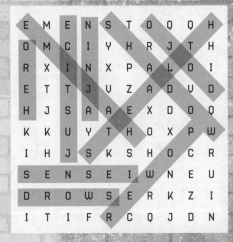

E	M	E	N	S	T	O	Q	Q	H
O	M	C	I	Y	H	R	J	T	H
R	X	I	N	X	P	A	L	O	I
E	T	T	J	U	Z	A	D	U	D
H	J	S	A	A	E	X	D	O	Q
K	K	U	Y	T	H	O	X	P	W
I	H	J	S	K	S	H	O	C	R
S	E	N	S	E	I	W	N	E	U
D	R	O	W	S	E	R	K	Z	I
I	T	I	F	R	C	Q	J	D	N

PAGE 34

4 and 6

PAGE 38

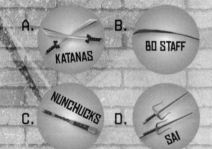